The blue rabbit
and
Flowers for Miss Barar

Hannie Truijens

Illustrated by Anna Hancock

Nelson

The blue rabbit

Mollie wasn't very happy.
They were having art and Mollie
didn't like art.
Her drawings were never any good and
her paintings always looked muddy.
Today they were doing tie-and-dye.
Miss Waterford, the art teacher, was
telling them how to do it but
Mollie wasn't listening.

Miss Waterford told the children
to start with light colours,
but Mollie started with dark green.
The children then tied their cloths with
string and dipped them in
the next colour.
Mollie dipped her cloth in dark brown.

When the cloths were finished the
children untied the strings.
They all had lovely cloths – except
for Mollie.
Mollie's cloth looked as if it had
fallen in the mud.
"It's just as bad as my paintings,"
said Mollie.
She threw her cloth in the corner and
went to play with the class rabbit.

Miss Waterford and the children went
outside to hang up their cloths to dry.
Mollie didn't want her ugly brown cloth.
She stayed in the classroom and
opened the rabbit cage.
She took the white rabbit in her arms.
It was soft and cuddly and much more fun
than tie-and-dye.

The rabbit was bored.
It jumped out of Mollie's arms and
started to run around the classroom.
It ran around the bucket of orange dye
and then around the bucket of red dye.
Mollie ran after the rabbit.
She wanted to catch it before Miss
Waterford came back.

The children came back into
the classroom.
They shouted when they saw the rabbit
running around the buckets of dye.
The rabbit was frightened by the shouting
and hopped up on a chair.
"Now I've got you," shouted Mollie, and
she ran to grab the rabbit.
She knocked over the bucket of yellow
dye.

The rabbit jumped off the chair just
before Mollie could reach it.
It landed in the bucket of blue dye.
Miss Waterford came into the classroom.
"Save the rabbit," she cried.
Mollie dived at the bucket of blue dye.
She knocked over the bucket of green
dye, but she did save the rabbit.

The rabbit shivered and sneezed the dye out of its nose.

Miss Waterford dried it on some old towels and cloths.

She rubbed it until it was quite dry, so that it wouldn't catch a cold.

Mollie was feeling very sorry for the rabbit.

The rabbit didn't catch a cold, but
it did stay blue.
"You were naughty to let the rabbit out
of the cage," said Miss Waterford, "but
you did save it."
Mollie looked at her hands and her feet.
"The rabbit is blue," she said, "but
I am tie-dyed."
"And so is the classroom floor," said
Miss Waterford.

Flowers for Miss Barar

None of the children in Miss Barar's
class went out to play at break.
They were all in the corner of the
classroom.
They were talking about Miss Barar's
birthday.
They didn't know what to get her
for her birthday.

"Let's get her some chocolates," said Mollie.

"She doesn't like chocolates," said Fred.

"Let's get her some pretty hankies," said Nancy.

"She has lots of hankies," said Larry.

"Let's get her some flowers," said Mollie.

"Everybody likes flowers."

12

The children agreed that they would all
bring one flower from home.
Mollie said that she would bring a vase.
"We must all draw a card for her," said
Fred.
"And write a poem on the card," said Larry.
The next morning Miss Barar had a very
big bunch of flowers on her table.
They looked lovely in Mollie's vase.

Miss Barar was very pleased with
the surprise.
She put her nose in the bunch of flowers
to smell them.
"A - a - a - A - A - **ATISHOO**," said Miss
Barar.
She felt in her pocket for a hanky but
she didn't have one.
"I have a hanky for you, Miss Barar," said
Nancy.

The children all sang Happy Birthday and then Miss Barar opened the cards.
She looked at all the pictures and then read the poems.
All the poems were lovely, but Larry's poem was the nicest of all.
Miss Barar read it out to the class.

"Our teacher, Miss Barar,
Has a birthday today.
So we said we'd all pick
One flower on the way.

One flower from each child
Will make a big bunch.
And maybe Miss Barar
Will treat us at lunch."

16

"I did bring a treat for you," said
Miss Barar.
"But we needn't wait for lunch.
I will give it to you now."
Miss Barar took a big tin of biscuits out
of the cupboard.
She held out the tin so that each child
could choose a biscuit.

17

When Miss Barar came to Nancy she started
sneezing.

"A - a - a - A - A - **ATISHOO**," she said.

She sneezed again and again.

The biscuits started to slide out
of the tin.

Nancy quickly held out her skirt.

All the biscuits fell into her skirt.

"**ATISHOO, ATISHOO, ATISHOO**," said Miss
Barar.

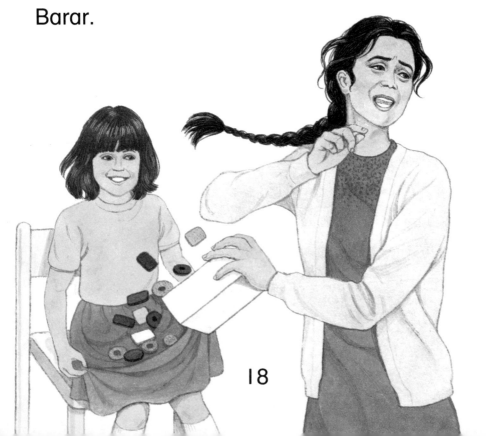

Miss Barar looked very unhappy.

"I'm sorry, children," she said, "but I can't keep the flowers in the classroom.

They are making me sneeze.

If they stay here I will do nothing but

… a - a - a - A - A - **ATISHOO**."

Fred took the flowers out of the classroom.

The children were sad about the flowers.

After break the children had art.
Miss Waterford asked them why they looked sad.
Larry told her about the flowers for Miss Barar.
"I have a good idea," said Miss Waterford.
"I will show you how to make a paper flower.
Than you can all give Miss Barar a flower which won't make her sneeze."

Even Mollie made a lovely paper flower.
"This is better than tie-and-dye,"
she said.
Miss Waterford made a pretty paper vase
for the flowers.
When the children went back to their
classroom Fred hid the flowers behind
his back.
When Miss Barar wasn't looking he quickly
put the flowers on the table.

21

When Miss Barar went back to the table
she saw the paper flowers.

"You can smell these, Miss Barar," said
Mollie.

"They won't make you sneeze," said Nancy.

"And you can keep them for ever," said Fred.

Miss Barar loved the paper flowers.

She gave all the children another biscuit
and she didn't sneeze once.

"What shall we do with the real flowers?"
said Mollie at lunch break.
"Let's give them to Mr Abbot,"
said Larry.
"He is always so grumpy.
Maybe the flowers will cheer him up."
The children took the flowers
to Mr Abbot.
He was the class five teacher.

"What's this?" said Mr Abbot when the children walked into his classroom.
"Flowers for you, Mr Abbot," said Nancy.
"What for?" said Mr Abbot.
"To make you happy," said Fred.
Mr Abbot put his nose in the flowers.
"Er - e - e - e - e," said Mr Abbot.
The children waited for him to sneeze.
"Er - er - thank you very much," he said.